POLICE

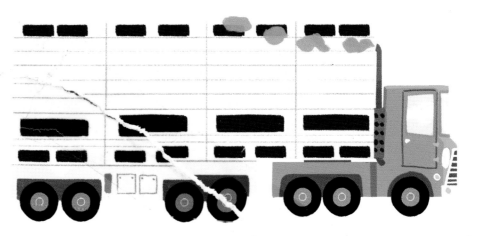

JANE'S TOWING

HOWLIDAY TOURS

To David, Ellie and Finnemore – M.R.

To Mama and Papa – J.T.

First published in Great Britain in 2021 by Andersen Press Ltd., 20 Vauxhall Bridge Roa...
Text copyright © Michelle Robinson 2021. Illustra...
The rights of Michelle Robinson and Jez Tuya to be identified as the auth...
them in accordance with the Copyright, Designs and Patents Act, 1988...
1 2 3 4 5 6 7 8 9 10   British Library Cataloguing in P...

RED LORRY, YELLOW LORRY

Michelle Robinson   Jez Tuya

Andersen Press

Red lorry, yellow lorry.

Red lorry, yellow lorry.

Tug lorry. Tow lorry.

Steady as you go, lorry!

Empty lorry,

load lorry.

Straight back on the road, lorry.

Busy lorry, bin lorry. Throw the whole lot in, lorry.

SQUEEZE, lorry! CRUSH, lorry! Never in a rush, lorry.

Lift, lorry. Shift, lorry.

Shove away the drift lorry.

Blare, lorry!

Blink, lorry!

What's in there,
d'you think, lorry?

Sheep lorry?

Cow lorry!

Can you spot the plough, lorry?

Wide lorry... TALL lorry!
Parked behind a wall lorry.

Someone needs a clean lorry.
Just where have you BEEN, lorry?!

Rolling...

dumping, tipping...

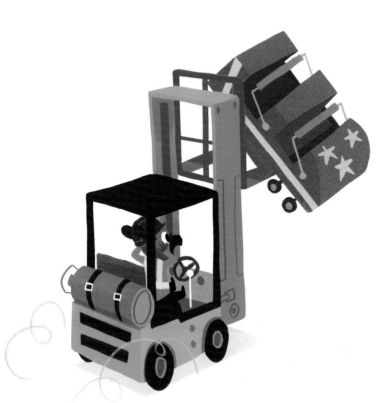

lifting!

Ladder raising,

dirt pile shifting.

Climbing, squashing...

spilling, mixing.

Biffing, breaking...

...building, fixing!
Pushing and pulling and
heaving and towing.

The going gets tough and
the trucks keep going.

Red lorry, yellow lorry.
Which one would you drive?
Blue lorry? Green lorry?

One
two
three
four
five!

On the road all day, lorry.

On the road

all night!

Pick a slower gear,
lorry...

Engines off...

Beep tight!